C000265427

RUDE RUGBY

SONGS

Jamien Bailey

www.booksbyboxer.com

Published in the UK by
Books By Boxer, Leeds, LS13 4BS
© Books By Boxer 2016
All Rights Reserved

ISBN: 9781909732360

RUDE RUGBY SONGS

The singing of bawdy songs is generally
a male thing though lots of women
quite enjoy hearing them and will join
in the singing if the mood takes. In fact,
many of the rudest and crudest were
plucked from the songbooks of women's
rugby clubs! Genteel ladies who should
know better!
(Know better how to 'out-shock' their
male counterparts, more like!)
Rude Rugby Songs are tasteless,
explicit, crude, downright filthy and
many are disgustingly sexist but, some
are very, very funny, if you like this
sort of thing. Some are quite poetic,
disarmingly witty and with an attention
to rhyme and metre usually more often

found in classical prose... but not many of them!

Of course, Rude Rugby Songs are not really rugby songs at all; most come from the armed forces, often composed during wars where humour and light relief were much in demand. Almost all the well-known bawdy songs are more than 50 years old and some stem as far back as the 16th century, from the rich British naval tradition of sea shanties that became corrupted along the way. Some follow the patterns of well-known tunes and these are indicated, if available.

The sporting fraternity, particularly rugby players (male and female) and associates, are particularly good at articulating and improvising a good filthy song. Thus, the British tradition of bawdy songs, initiated in time immemorial, before even Shakespeare called, "Go bring me a lass", is kept alive and kicking in clubs and coaches. (The bus type, NOT the human type!) And we are proud to continue this noble cause because, after all, it's humour and not the Hokey Kokey, that it's all about!

CHARLOTTE THE HARLOT

Another tale of a poor but honest, lady of ill repute.

Way down on the prairie
Where cow plop is thick,
Where women are women
And cowpokes cum quick,
There lived pretty Charlotte,
The girl we adore,
The pride of the prairie,
The cowpunchers' whore.

Chorus:
It's Charlotte the harlot,
The girl we adore,
The pride of the prairie,
The cowpunchers' whore.

She's dirty, she's vulgar,
She spits in the street,
Why whenever you see her,
She's always in heat.
She'll lay fur a dollar,
Take less or take more,
The pride of the prairie,
The cowpunchers' whore.

Chorus:
It's Charlotte the harlot,
The girl we adore,
The pride of the prairie,
The cowpunchers' whore.

One day in the canyon,
No pants on her quim,
A rattlesnake saw her
And flung himself in,
Charlotte the harlot gave
Cowboys the frights,
The only vagina that
Rattles and bites.

Chorus:
It's Charlotte the harlot,
The girl we adore,
The pride of the prairie,
The cowpunchers' whore.

One day on the prairie,
While riding along,
My seat in the saddle,
The reins on my dong,
Who should I meet
But the girl I adore,
The pride of the prairie,
The cowpunchers' whore.

Chorus:
It's Charlotte the harlot,
The girl we adore,
The pride of the prairie,
The cowpunchers' whore.

I got off my pony,
I reached for her crack,
The damn thing was rattling
And biting me back,
I took out my pistol,
I aimed for its head,
I missed the damned rattler
And shot her instead.

Chorus:
It's Charlotte the harlot,
The girl we adore,
The pride of the prairie,
The cowpunchers' whore.

Her funeral procession
Was forty miles long,
With a chorus of cowpunchers
Singing this song:
"Here lies a young maiden
Who never kept score,
The pride of the prairie,
The cowpunchers' whore."

R.I.P.
Charlotte

MASTURBATION SONG 1

A jolly ditty about those who choose to amuse by self abuse!

You don't need to use a condom,
You don't need a dental dam,
You don't need to say "I Love You" or
"Here's fifty dollars, ma'am."

Don't need to spring for dinner,
Or wear all that sexy stuff,
All you need's a set of fingers
And a wanker or a muff,
'Cause everybody's doin' it,
All across the land,
Masturbators of America,
Give yourselves a hand!

It's natural, and organic,
It's easy and it's fun,
If you don't know how to do,
It ask your parents how it's done,
You don't need a special license.

You don't need a special skill,
Just unzip and slip your grip between, your
Hips and get a thrill,
'Cause everybody's doin' it,
And boy does it feel grand,
Masturbators of America,
Give yourselves a hand!

You can do it in the bathroom,
You can do it in your bed,
You can do it at a concert
While you watch the Grateful Dead,
You can rub it with some lotion.
Arnold Shwartzenegger pounds it,
Michael Jackson jacks it off,

Your attitude will soften,
Your horizons will expand,
Masturbators of America,
Give yourself a hand!

WALKING ROUND IN WOMEN'S UNDERWEAR

This favourite is sang to the tune of Walking in a Winter Wonder Land. Nothing like this one to liven up the Christmas party!

Lacy things... the wife is missin',
Didn't ask... her permission,
I'm wearin' her clothes,
Her silk pantyhose,
Walkin' round in women's underwear.

In the store... there's a teddy,
Little straps... like spaghetti,
It holds me so tight,
Like handcuffs at night,
Walkin' round in women's underwear.
In the office there's a guy named Melvin,
He pretends that I am Murphy Brown.

He'll say, "Are you ready?"
I'll say,"Whoa, Man!"
"Let's wait until our wives are out of town!"

Later on, if you wanna,
We can dress... like Madonna,
Put on some eyeshade,
And join the parade,
Walkin' round in women's underwear!

Lacy things... missin',
Didn't ask... permission,
Wearin' her clothes,
Her silk pantyhose,
Walkin' round in women's underwear.

Walkin' round in women's underwear,
Walkin' round in women's underwear!

THE MASTURBATION SONG 2

Here we go again. These boys truly delight in their predilection for onanism. However, the redeeming feature of this rendering is it is sung to the tune of, 'Funiculi, Funicula', a classical piece of Neopolitan music written in 1880 to commemorate the first funicular railway on Mount Vesuvius in Italy.

(Sing to the tune of 'Funiculi, Funicula')

Last night I tried my hand at masturbation,
It felt so good, I knew it would.
Tonight I will repeat the operation,
It feels so nice, I'll do it twice.
First, I'll do the short strokes,
Straight up and down,
Straight up and down.
And then, I'll do the long strokes,
Around and around, around and around.

Slam it, ram it, hit it on the floor,
Wrap it, slap it on the bed post
And the door.
Some people think that
Sexual intercourse is grand,
But I would rather stay at home,
And do it with my hand.

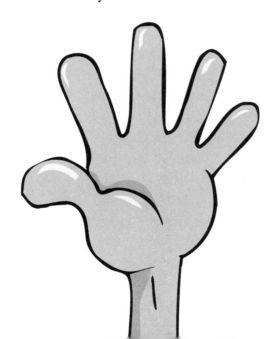

MY GOD HOW THE MONEY ROLLS IN

A resourceful family promoting the virtues of 'privates' enterprise.

My father makes books on the corner,
My mother makes second-hand gin,
My sister makes love for a dollar,
My god, how the money rolls in.

Chorus:
Rolls in, rolls in,
My god how the money rolls in,
Rolls in, rolls in, rolls in,
My god, how the money rolls in.

My brother's a poor missionary,
He saves fallen women from sin,
He'll save you a tart for five dollars,
My god, how the money rolls in.

Chorus:
Rolls in, rolls in,
My god how the money rolls in,
Rolls in, rolls in, rolls in,
My god, how the money rolls in.

Now my grandma sells
Cheap prophylactics,
She punctures the head with a pin,
Grandad gets rich,
From vasectomy snips,
My god, how the money rolls in.

Chorus:
Rolls in, rolls in,
My god how the money rolls in,
Rolls in, rolls in, rolls in,
My god, how the money rolls in.

FOUR AND TWENTY VIRGINS

A jolly little ditty with a lively chorus. The tune goes something like The Blaydon Races... but not quite! This song is perfect for a big finish, with harmonies on the final chorus!

Four and twenty virgins
Came down from Inverness.
And when the ball was over,
There were four and twenty less.

Chorus:
Singing, balls to your partner,
Arse against the wall.
If you never get shagged on Saturday night,
You'll never get shagged at all.

The village vicar he was there
Dressed in all his shroud.
Swinging on the chandelier
And pissing on the crowd.

Chorus:
Singing, balls to your partner,
Arse against the wall.
If you never get shagged on Saturday night,
You'll never get shagged at all.

The vicar's wife she was there
Sitting by the fire,
Knitting rubber johnnies
With a ball of rubber wire.

Chorus:
Singing, balls to your partner,
Arse against the wall.
If you never get shagged on Saturday night,
You'll never get shagged at all.

Farmer Giles he was there,
His scythe was in his hand,
And every time he swung around,
He circumcised the band.

Chorus:
Singing, balls to your partner,
Arse against the wall.
If you never get shagged on Saturday night,
You'll never get shagged at all.

The Bride was in the parlour
Explaining to the groom,
That the vagina, not the rectum, is the
Entrance to the womb.

Chorus:
Singing, balls to your partner,
Arse against the wall.
If you never get shagged on Saturday night,
You'll never get shagged at all.

There was shagging in the hallways,
Shagging on the stairs.
You could not hear the music
For the swish of pubic hair.

Chorus:
Singing, balls to your partner,
Arse against the wall.
If you never get shagged on Saturday night,
You'll never get shagged at all.

The village policeman he was there,
A credit to the force.
They caught him in the stable block,
Tossing off a horse.

Chorus:
Singing, balls to your partner,
Arse against the wall.
If you never get shagged on Saturday night,
You'll never get shagged at all.

The village cripple, he was there,
He wasn't up to much.
He lined the girls against the wall,
And fucked'em with his crutch.

Chorus:
Singing, balls to your partner,
Arse against the wall.
If you never get shagged on Saturday night,
You'll never get shagged at all.

The village idiot he was there,
Sitting on a pole.
Pulling his foreskin over his head
And whistling through the hole.

Chorus:
Singing, balls to your partner,
Arse against the wall.
If you never get shagged on Saturday night,
You'll never get shagged at all.

The idiot's brother he was there,
Can you imagine that.
Amusing himself by abusing himself,
And catching it in his hat.

Chorus:
Singing, balls to your partner,
Arse against the wall.
If you never get shagged on Saturday night,
You'll never get shagged at all.

And when the ball was over,
Everyone confessed,
They'd all enjoyed the dancing
But the shagging was a mess.

Chorus:
Singing, balls to your partner,
Arse against the wall.
If you never get shagged on Saturday night,
You'll never get shagged at all.

THE GOOD SHIP VENUS

More of a lively monologue than a song, with an iambic cadence on the third line.

We were on the good ship Venus,
By Christ you should have seen us,
The figurehead was a whore in bed
Sucking an elephant's penis.

The captain's name was Lugger,
By Christ he was a bugger,
He wasn't fit to shovel shit,
From one ship to another.

And the second mate was Andy,
By Christ he had a dandy ,
Till they crushed his cock on a jagged rock,
For cummin in the brandy.

The third mate's name was Morgan,
By God he was a gorgon,
From half past eight he played till late,
Upon the captain's organ.

The bosun's name was Carter,
By God he was a farter,
When the wind wouldn't blow
And the ship wouldn't go,
They'd get Carter, the farter, to start her.

The captain's wife was Mabel,
And by God she weren't half able.
She gave the crew their daily screw,
Upon the galley table.

The captain's daughter Charlotte,
Was born and bred a harlot,
Her thighs at night were lily white,
By morning they were scarlet.

The cabin boy was Kipper,
By Christ he was a nipper,
He stuffed his ass with broken glass
And circumcised the skipper.

The captain's lovely daughter,
Liked swimming in the water.
Delighted squeals came when some eels,
Found her sexual quarter.

The cook his name was Freeman,
And he was a dirty demon,
And he fed the crew on menstrual stew,
And hymens fried in semen.

When we reached our station
Through skillful navigation,
The ship got sunk in a wave of spunk,
From too much fornication.

We were on the good ship Venus,
By Christ you should have seen us,
The figurehead was a whore in bed,
Sucking an elephant's penis.

BARNACLE BILL THE SAILOR

**A good old fashioned sea shanty. This allows scope for latent thespian skills as the song is written for male and female parts, or deep voice and girly voice from the same fella.
Sung to the tune of 'Barnacle Bill the Sailor.'
Yes, there is a clean version!**

Woman's Voice:
Who's that knocking at my door?
Who's that knocking at my door?
Who's that knocking at my door?
Cried the fair young maiden.

Man's Voice:
Oh, it's only me from across the sea.
Cried Barnacle Bill the Sailor.
Woman's Voice:
Why are you knocking at my door?
Why are you knocking at my door?

Why are you knocking at my door?
Cried the fair young maiden.

Man's Voice:
'Cos I'm young enough,
And ready and tough.
Cried Barnacle Bill the Sailor.

W: Will you take me to the dance?
M: To hell with the dance,
    down with your pants.

W: You can sleep upon the floor.
M: I'll not sleep on the floor,
    you dirty whore.
W: You can sleep upon the mat.
M: Bugger the mat you can't fuck that.

W: You can sleep upon the stairs.
M: Oh, fuck the stairs,
    they haven't got hairs.

W: What's that running up my blouse?
M: It's only me mitt to grab yer tit.

W: You can sleep between my tits.
M: Oh, bugger your tits,
   they give me the shits.

W: You can sleep between my thighs.
M: Bugger your thighs,
   they're covered in flies.

W: You can sleep within my cunt.
M: Oh, bugger your cunt,
   but I'll fuck for a stunt.

W: What's that running in and out?
M: It's only me cock,
   it's as hard as a rock.

W: What's that running down my leg?
M: It's only me shot that missed yer twot.

W: What if my parents should find out?
M: We'll eat your ma and blow your pa.

W: What if my mother should disagree?
M: If yer ma'll agree we'll make it three.

W: What if we should get VD?
M: We'll pick the sores and fuck some more.

W: What if we should get the clap?
M: Gotta be willin' to take penicillin.

W: What if we should have a boy?
M: He'll play rugby and fuck like me.

W: What if you should go to jail?
M: I'll pick the lock with my 10ft cock.

W: What if we should go to prison?
M: I'll swing my balls and knock
   down the walls.

RUGBY MEN

A rather disparaging image of our rough tough, rugby heroes, but real men are not afraid of being the butt of the joke, even in 'the joke of the butt'! This tune is the familiar... 'This old man, he played one.'

Rugby men, they play one,
They all take it up the bum,

With a nick nack paddy whack
Give the boy a bone,
Rugby men have sex alone!

Rugby men, they play two,
They can't get it up for you,

With a nick nack paddy whack
Give the boy a bone,
Rugby men have sex alone!

Rugby men, they play three,
They like to kiss us where we wee,

With a nick nack paddy whack
Give the boy a bone,
Rugby men have sex alone!

Rugby men, they play four,
They like to take it up the back-trap-door,

With a nick nack paddy whack
Give the boy a bone,
Rugby men have sex alone!

Rugby men, they play five,
They can't keep a girl alive,

With a nick nack paddy whack
Give the boy a bone,
Rugby men have sex alone!

Rugby men, they play six,
Little men with little dicks,

With a nick nack paddy whack
Give the boy a bone,
Rugby men have sex alone!

Rugby men, they play seven,
They can't take their women to heaven,

With a nick nack paddy whack
Give the boy a bone,
Rugby men have sex alone!

Rugby men, they play eight,
All they do is masturbate,

With a nick nack paddy whack
Give the boy a bone,
Rugby men have sex alone!

Rugby men, they play nine,
All they do is moan and whine,

With a nick nack paddy whack
Give the boy a bone,
Rugby men have sex alone!

Rugby men, they play ten,
Little boys who think they're men,

With a nick nack paddy whack
Give the boy a bone,
Rugby men have sex alone!

YOU CAN TELL BY MY SMELL

Probably the most distasteful ditty of bodily functions that we have ever passed for print.

Though there are a few redeeming features, such as the clever introduction of the conjugated protein, haemoglobin, into one of the verses.

Verdict: disgustingly funny!

You can tell by my smell,
That I'm not feeling well,
When the time of the month comes around.
You can tell by my smell,
That I'm not feeling well,
When the time of the month comes around.

Chorus:
Oh, we are the girls from the Tampax Factory,
Our products are clean, clear and sound
We've got small, medium, large,
Super duper, fill-a-barge,
When the time of the month comes around!

You can tell by my stench,
That I've got a gammy trench,
When the time of the month comes around.
You can tell by my stench,
That I've got a gammy trench,
When the time of the month comes around.

Chorus:
Oh, we are the girls from the Tampax Factory,
Our products are clean, clear and sound
We've got small, medium, large,
Super duper, fill-a-barge,
When the time of the month comes around!

You can tell by my string,
That you won't be doing a thing,
When the time of the month comes around.
You can tell by my string,
That you won't be doing a thing,
When the time of the month comes around.

Chorus:
Oh, we are the girls from the Tampax Factory,
Our products are clean, clear and sound
We've got small, medium, large,
Super duper, fill-a-barge,
When the time of the month comes around!

You can tell by my sheet,
That you won't be giving meat,
When the time of the month comes around.
You can tell by my sheet,
That you won't be giving meat,
When the time of the month comes around.

Chorus:
Oh, we are the girls from the Tampax Factory,
Our products are clean, clear and sound
We've got small, medium, large,
Super duper, fill-a-barge,
When the time of the month comes around!

You can tell by my rope,
That you haven't got a hope,
When the time of the month comes around.
You can tell by my rope,
That you haven't got a hope,
When the time of the month comes around.

Chorus:
Oh, we are the girls from the Tampax Factory,
Our products are clean, clear and sound
We've got small, medium, large,
Super duper, fill-a-barge,
When the time of the month comes around!

You can tell by my frown,
That you won't be going down,
When the time of the month comes around.
You can tell by my frown,
That you won't be going down,
When the time of the month comes around.

Chorus:
Oh, we are the girls from the Tampax Factory,
Our products are clean, clear and sound
We've got small, medium, large,
Super duper, fill-a-barge,
When the time of the month comes around!

You can tell by my frown,
That you won't be going down,
When the time of the month comes around.
You can tell by my frown,
That you won't be going down,
When the time of the month comes around.

Chorus:
Oh, we are the girls from the Tampax Factory,
Our products are clean, clear and sound
We've got small, medium, large,
Super duper, fill-a-barge,
When the time of the month comes around!

You can tell by my taste,
That it isn't salmon paste,
When the time of the month comes around.
You can tell by my taste,
That it isn't salmon paste,
When the time of the month comes around.

Chorus:
Oh, we are the girls from the Tampax Factory,
Our products are clean, clear and sound
We've got small, medium, large,
Super duper, fill-a-barge,
When the time of the month comes around!

You can tell by my moaning,
That I'm losing haemoglobin,
When the time of the month comes around.
You can tell by my moaning,
That I'm losing haemoglobin,
When the time of the month comes around

Chorus:
Oh, we are the girls from the Tampax Factory,
Our products are clean, clear and sound
We've got small, medium, large,
Super duper, fill-a-barge,
When the time of the month comes around!

You can tell by my feel,
That I'm starting to congeal,
When the time of the month comes around.
You can tell by my feel,
That I'm starting to congeal,
When the time of the month comes around.

Chorus:
Oh, we are the girls from the Tampax Factory,
Our products are clean, clear and sound
We've got small, medium, large,
Super duper, fill-a-barge,
When the time of the month comes around!

You can tell by her reek,
That it must be Dawson's Creek!
When the time of the month comes around.
You can tell by her reek,
That it must be Dawson's Creek!
When the time of the month comes around.

Chorus:
Oh, we are the girls from the Tampax Factory,
Our products are clean, clear and sound
We've got small, medium, large,
Super duper, fill-a-barge,
When the time of the month comes around!

FUCK 'EM ALL

Derived from the favourite army song, a satirical take on the top brass, Bless 'em all (the long and the short and the tall). Always a favourite, perhaps because it has a good tune.

FUCK 'em all, fuck 'em all, fuck 'em all,
The long and the short and the tall,
FUCK all the blond cunts
And all the brunettes,
Don't be too choosy, just fuck all you gets,
'Cause we're saying goodbye to them all,
As back to the barracks we crawl,
You'll get no erection at short-arm inspection,
So prick up you men, fuck 'em all.

FUCK 'em all, fuck 'em all, fuck 'em all,
The long and the short and the tall,
FUCK all the cunts 'til your knob
Breaks it in two,

You'll get no loving where you're going to,
'Cause we're saying goodbye to them all,
As back to the barracks we crawl,
So get your big prick up and give it a stick up,
Cheer up my lads, fuck 'em all!

YORKSHIRE LIFE

It's not a song but we thought you'd like it.

Down in't garage chauffeur lies,
Master's wife between his thighs,
Master's voice comes from afar,
Stop fucking't wife and start' t' fucking car.

ALL THE NICE GIRLS

It's short and sweet, just like the subject matter, and a good tune, too.

All the nice girls love a candle,
All the nice girls love a wick,
For there's something about a candle,
It feels so like a prick.
Nice and greasy, slips in easy,
It's the ladies pride and joy,
It's been up the Queen of Spain,
And it's going up again,
Ship ahoy! Sailor boy!

OTHER THINGS TO TWIDDLE

A sentimental old sea song of the hardships a sailor's wife must endure.

When the ships all get to sailing
And the men are often gone,
What about the women who
Are up and left alone?
Do you think they sit and twiddle thumbs,
Until the men come home?
There are other things to twiddle
When a girl's left on her own.

Chorus:
And it's twiddly-aye-dee-aye-dee-aye,
Twiddly-ate-dee-ay,
Often times a man can leave
You broken with dismay,
Twiddly-aye-dee-aye-dee-aye,
Twiddly-ate-dee-ay,
There's other things to twiddle
When your man has gone away.

Sweet Miss Nancy Johnson
Was as fair as any maid,
Her true love went a-voyaging,
A sailor-man by trade,
"Keep the fires burning, love,"
Those were the words he spoke,
So she found herself another man
To keep the fires stoked.

Chorus:
And it's twiddly-aye-dee-aye-dee-aye,
Twiddly-ate-dee-ay,
Often times a man can leave
You broken with dismay,
Twiddly-aye-dee-aye-dee-aye,
Twiddly-ate-dee-ay,
There's other things to twiddle
When your man has gone away.

I remember Nelly, she was young
And she was gay,
She won the heart of Captain Dann
Until he went away,
He left her high and dry
With but a kiss upon the chin,
But as his ship was sailing out,
Another ship sailed in.

Chorus:
And it's twiddly-aye-dee-aye-dee-aye,
Twiddly-ate-dee-ay,
Often times a man can leave
You broken with dismay,
Twiddly-aye-dee-aye-dee-aye,
Twiddly-ate-dee-ay,
There's other things to twiddle
When your man has gone away.

Lucy Duncan's man came home
And knocked upon her door,
She was as glad to see him as
She'd ever been before,
He left her lying on the bed
But Lucy didn't care,
For the fellow in the closet, too,
Could use a little air.

Chorus:
And it's twiddly-aye-dee-aye-dee-aye,
Twiddly-ate-dee-ay,
Often times a man can leave
You broken with dismay,
Twiddly-aye-dee-aye-dee-aye,
Twiddly-ate-dee-ay,
There's other things to twiddle
When your man has gone away.

Now, you hear a lot of stories,
'Bout the sailor and his sport,
About how every lad,
Has got a girl in every port,
Well, if you'll add up two and two,
You'll figure out right quick,
It's just because a girl
Has got a lad on every ship.

Chorus:
And it's twiddly-aye-dee-aye-dee-aye,
Twiddly-ate-dee-ay,
Often times a man can leave
You broken with dismay,
Twiddly-aye-dee-aye-dee-aye,
Twiddly-ate-dee-ay,
There's other things to twiddle
When your man has gone away.

THE LOBSTER

**A sailor's hauling song from way back. A sad
end for the lobster. The chorus goes along
the same tuneful lines as 'Four and Twenty
Virgins'.**

Oh Mr Fisherman
Back from the sea,
Have you a lobster
You can sell to me?

Chorus:
Singing hi tidly hi ti, shit or bust,
Never let your goolies dangle in the dust.

Well yes sir, yes sir,
I have two,
And the biggest of the bastards
I will sell to you.

Chorus:
Singing hi tidly hi ti, shit or bust,
Never let your goolies dangle in the dust.

I got the lobster home,
I couldn't find a dish,
So I put it in the pot
Where the Missus has a piss.

Chorus:
Singing hi tidly hi ti, shit or bust,
Never let your goolies dangle in the dust.

Early next morning,
The old woman rose,
Up went her nightie and
She let the waters flow.
At first she gave a scream,
And then she gave a grunt,
And she leapt around the room
With a lobster on her cunt

Chorus:
Singing hi tidly hi ti, shit or bust,
Never let your goolies dangle in the dust.

I grabbed the poker,
She grabbed the broom,
We chased that fucking lobster
All around the room.

Chorus:
Singing hi tidly hi ti, shit or bust,
Never let your goolies dangle in the dust.

I hit it in the back.
I hit it in the side,
I hit it in the bollocks
Until the bastard died.

Chorus:
Singing hi tidly hi ti, shit or bust,
Never let your goolies dangle in the dust.

The moral of the story,
The moral it is this,
Always have a shuftie
Before you have a piss.

Chorus:
Singing hi tidly hi ti, shit or bust,
Never let your goolies dangle in the dust.

This is my story,
I'll tell you no more,
There's an apple up my arsehole
And you can have the core.

Chorus:
Singing hi tidly hi ti, shit or bust,
Never let your goolies dangle in the dust.

There's another end to my story,
I don't give a fuck,
There's an orange up my arsehole,
You can have a suck.

Chorus:
Singing hi tidly hi ti, shit or bust,
Never let your goolies dangle in the dust.

THE ALPHABET

A lexicon of lewdness based on the tune of the delightful children's song 'A frog he would a wooing go'. Is nothing sacred?

A is for ARSEHOLE all covered in shit,
"Hey Ho," Said Roley,
And B is the BASTARD who's rolling in it.

Chorus:
Up 'em and stuff 'em, shag 'em or buff 'em,
"Hey Ho," says Anthony Roley.

C is for Clitoris all dripping with piss, "Hey Ho," Said Roley,
And D is the Devil who gives it a kiss.

Chorus:
Up 'em and stuff 'em, shag 'em or buff 'em,
"Hey Ho," says Anthony Roley.

E is for Enuch with only one ball,
"Hey Ho," Said Roley,
And F is for Fucker with no balls at all.

Chorus:
Up 'em and stuff 'em, shag 'em or buff 'em,
"Hey Ho," says Anthony Roley.

G is for gangrene, gonorrhoea and gout,
"Hey Ho," Said Roley,
And H is the Harlot that spreads it about.

Chorus:
Up 'em and stuff 'em, shag 'em or buff 'em,
"Hey Ho," says Anthony Roley.

I is the Itch, which comes with the crabs,
"Hey Ho," Said Roley,
And J is for jamrag all covered in scabs.

Chorus:
Up 'em and stuff 'em, shag 'em or buff 'em,
"Hey Ho," says Anthony Roley.

K is the king of the Cannibal Isles,
"Hey Ho," Said Roley,
And L is the lover who stuffs back his piles.

Chorus:
Up 'em and stuff 'em, shag 'em or buff 'em,
"Hey Ho," says Anthony Roley.

M is the monk in the monastery bright,
"Hey Ho," Said Roley,
And N is the nun who sees him alright.

Chorus:
Up 'em and stuff 'em, shag 'em or buff 'em,
"Hey Ho," says Anthony Roley.

O is the orifice all ragged and red,
"Hey Ho," Said Roley,
And P is the penis, that fucks it in bed.

Chorus:
Up 'em and stuff 'em, shag 'em or buff 'em,
"Hey Ho," says Anthony Roley.

Q is the quaker who shat in his hat, "Hey
Ho," Said Roley,
And R is the rector who ate what he shat.

Chorus:
Up 'em and stuff 'em, shag 'em or buff 'em,
"Hey Ho," says Anthony Roley.

S is for shitpan topped up to the brim,
"Hey Ho," Said Roley,
And T are the turds that are floating within.

Chorus:
Up 'em and stuff 'em, shag 'em or buff 'em,
"Hey Ho," says Anthony Roley.

U is the Urchin a-pulling his pud,
"Hey Ho," Said Roley,
And V is the vicar who wished that he could.

Chorus:
Up 'em and stuff 'em, shag 'em or buff 'em,
"Hey Ho," says Anthony Roley.

W is for wanking, which is Oh! Such a farce!
"Hey Ho," Said Roley,
And X, Y, and Z you can stick up your arse!

Chorus:
Up 'em and stuff 'em, shag 'em or buff 'em,
"Hey Ho," says Anthony Roley.

ALL QUEERS TOGETHER

A song of it's time depicting strange animal behavior, with some quite intelligent phrasing, from the officers mess, at least.

The sexual life of a camel
Is stranger than anyone thinks

At the height of the mating season,
He tries to bugger the sphinx

But the sphinx's posterior orifice
Is blocked with the sands from the Nile

Which accounts for the hump on the camel
And the sphinx's inscrutable smile

Chorus:
Singing Bum Titty, Bum Titty, Titty Bum
Bum Titty Bum Titty ay,
Singing Bum Titty, Bum Titty, Titty Bum
Singing Bum Titty Bum Titty ay
'Cos we're all queers together
That's why we go around in pairs
Yes we're all queers together
Excuse us while we go upstairs

Now the sexual life of a bullfrog
Is hard to comprehend

At the height of the mating season
He tries to bugger his friend

But the arse of the average bullfrog
Is filled up with mucus and slime

Which accounts for the face of the bullfrog
And why he goes BURRRRRP all the time

Chorus:
Singing Bum Titty, Bum Titty, Titty Bum
Bum Titty Bum Titty ay,
Singing Bum Titty, Bum Titty, Titty Bum
Singing Bum Titty Bum Titty ay
'Cos we're all queers together
That's why we go around in pairs
Yes we're all queers together
Excuse us while we go upstairs

A biological paper from Oxford
By Harrison, Hunter and Hall

Has proven that the common hedgehog
Cannot be buggered at all

An alternative thesis from Cambridge
Has incontrovertibly shown

That comparative immunity from buggery
Is enjoyed by the hedgehog alone

1st Chorus:
Singing Bum Titty, Bum Titty, Titty Bum,
Bum Titty Bum Titty ay,
Singing, Bum Titty, Bum Titty, Titty Bum,
Singing, Bum Titty Bum Titty ay.

'Twas Christmas night in the harem,
The Eunuchs were standing there,

Watching the fair young maidens,
combing their pubic hair,

When the voice from the Sultan
Came echoing through the hall,

Saying what do you want for Christmas,
And the Eunuchs all answered BALLS.

2nd Chorus:
'Cos we're all queers together
That's why we go around in pairs
Yes we're all queers together
Excuse us while we go upstairs

SING US ANOTHER ONE

An effort to bring a tuneful rendering of limericks linked by a nostalgic, melancholy chorus. The tune allows an attempt for all and sundry to out-disgust the others by introducing their own rendition of their filthy, pernicious wit. There are zillions of limericks out there, with new ones being created by the minute, so we have limited this selection to ten.
(Ending with an uncharacteristically clean one!)

There was a young lady from Itching,
Sat scratching her crutch in the kitchen,
Her Mother said, "Rose,
It's pox I suppose,"
She said, "Bollocks,
Get on with your knitting."

Chorus:
That was a beautiful song,
Sing us another one,
Just like the other one,
Sing us another one do.

There was a young girl from Azores,
Whose body was covered in sores,
Even the dogs in the street,
Wouldn't eat the green meat,
That hung in festoons from her drawers.

Chorus:
That was a beautiful song,
Sing us another one,
Just like the other one,
Sing us another one do.

There was a young sailor from Brighton,
Who remarked to his girl, you've a tight one,
She replied, "Oh my soul,
You're in the wrong hole,
There's plenty of room in the right one.

Chorus:
That was a beautiful song,
Sing us another one,
Just like the other one,
Sing us another one do.

There once was a woman named Jill,
Who swallowed an exploding pill,
They found her vagina,
In North Carolina,
And her tits in a tree in Brazil!

Chorus:
That was a beautiful song,
Sing us another one,
Just like the other one,
Sing us another one do.

There was a young lady from Leeds,
Who swallowed a packet of seeds,
Within the hour,
her tits were a-flower,
And her arse was all covered in weeds.

Chorus:
That was a beautiful song,
Sing us another one,
Just like the other one,
Sing us another one do.

There once was a plumber from Lee
Who was plumbing his girl by the sea
She said, Stop your plumbing,
There's somebody coming!
Said the plumber, still plumbing... it's me!

Chorus:
That was a beautiful song,
Sing us another one,
Just like the other one,
Sing us another one do.

There once was a girl from Zeebrucke,
Who played with a small rubber sucker,
She found that it fit, the clit in her slit,
And now she needs no one to fuck her.

Chorus:
That was a beautiful song,
Sing us another one,
Just like the other one,
Sing us another one do.

There once was a young girl from Darjeeling,
Who danced with such sensual feeling,
There wasn't a word, or a sound that was heard,
Save for fly hole buttons hitting the ceiling

Chorus:
That was a beautiful song,
Sing us another one,
Just like the other one,
Sing us another one do.

There once was a man from Gosham,
Who took out his balls to wash 'em,
His wife said Jack, If you don't put them back,
I'll jump on the buggers and squash 'em.

Chorus:
That was a beautiful song,
Sing us another one,
Just like the other one,
Sing us another one do.

There was a young lady named Bright,
Who traveled much faster than light.
She set out one day, in a relative way,
And came back the previous night.

BOHEMIAN CURRY

To the tune of the classic Queen hit 'Bohemian Rhapsody', it's a mob cast production. You can separate your group into the several parts necessary for a fine performance, with a big finish. It's hilarious, especially if performed in a curry house. Air guitar solos are actively encouraged!

Naan-aan, just killed a man
Poppadom against his head
Had lime pickle, now he's dead.
Naan-aan, dinner just begun
But now I'm going to crap it all away.
Naan-aan, ooh-ooh
Didn't mean to make you cry,
Seen nothin' yet just see the loo tomorrow,
Curry on,
Curry on,
'Cause nothing really Madras.

Too late, my dinner's gone
Sends shivers up my spine
Rectum aching all the time.
Goodbye every bhaji,
I've got to go
Gotta leave you all behind
And use the loo.
Naan-aan, ooh ooh,
This Dopiaza's mild,
I sometimes wish we'd never
Come here at all...

(Guitar solo)

I see a little chicken tikka on the side,
Rogan Josh, Rogan Josh
Pass the chutney made of mango.
Vindaloo does nicely
Very very spicey... ME!
Biryani
(Biryani)

Biryani
(Biryani)
Biryani and a naan,
(A vindaloo loo looo...)
I've eaten balti, somebody help me
She's eaten balti, get her to a lavatory
All stand well back
'Cause this loo is quarantined.
Here it comes,
There it goes,
Technicolour yawn.
I chunder
No!
It's coming up again
(There she goes)
I chunder
It's coming up again
(There she goes)
It's coming up again,
(Up again)
Coming up again

(up again)
Here it comes again
(No no no no no no no no no No).
On my knees,
I'm on my knees,
I'm on my knees
Oh there she goes
This vindaloo is about to wreck my guts
Poor me... Poor me... Poor me!

(Guitar solo)

So you think you can chunder
And still it's alright?
So you want to eat curry
And drink beer all night?
Ohh maybe,
Now you'll puke like a baby,
Just had to come out,
Just had to come right out in here...

(Guitar solo)

Korma, saag or bhuna,
Balti, naan, bhaji.
Nothing makes a difference
Nothing makes a difference to me
(Anyway, my wind blows).

DUREX IS A GIRL'S BEST FRIEND

A superb take on the Marilyn classic.

A poke with a bloke may be quite incidental,
But Durex is a girl's best friend.
You may get the works
But you won't be parental.
As he slides it in,
You trust that good old latex skin
As he lets fly, none gets by
'Cos it's all gathered up in the end.
This little precaution
Avoids an abortion
Durex is a girl's best friend!

MAGIC MOMENTS

To the tune of the classic Perry Como song, but tainted by depravity. This will make any moment considerably less than magical!

I'll never forget
The strong smell of the sweat,
From under her armpit,
It wasn't the grass
That tickled her arse,
But my middle digit.

Magic moments,
When our two hearts are sharing,
Magic moments,
Filled with love.

Just for a lark
I went down the park,
And pissed on the flowers,
You sat on a rock
And played with my cock,
For hours and hours.

Magic moments,
When our two hearts are sharing,
Magic moments,
Filled with love.

We went to the sea
I knew it would be,
A time of emotion,
We laid on the sand
My prick in your hand,
I pissed in the ocean.

Magic moments,
When our two hearts are sharing,
Magic moments,
Filled with love.

THE ENGINEER

A tragic tale.

An engineer told me before he died,
And I've no reason to believe he lied,
That no matter how he tried and tried,
His girlfriend never could be satisfied,

Chorus:
And the stop-cock was left handed,
And the stop-cock was left handed,
And the stop-cock was left handed,
There was no easy way to stop that thing!

His girlfriend had a fanny so wide so wide,
That a telegraph pole wouldn't
Touch the sides,
And she could never be satisfied,
No matter how much he tried and tried.

Chorus:
And the stop-cock was left handed,
And the stop-cock was left handed,
And the stop-cock was left handed,
There was no easy way to stop that thing!

The engineer was a clever designer,
Taught and trained in South Carolina,
He measured the bore of her vagina,
And thought he could do finer
Than just fitting a liner.

Chorus:
And the stop-cock was left handed,
And the stop-cock was left handed,
And the stop-cock was left handed,
There was no easy way to stop that thing!

Then he built a fucking great machine,
It was slick and smooth
And squeaky and clean,
It chunted and grunted,
Powerful and mean,
And the whole darn thing
Was driven by steam.

Chorus:
And the stop-cock was left handed,
And the stop-cock was left handed,
And the stop-cock was left handed,
There was no easy way to stop that thing!

Round and round went a big wooden wheel,
And up and down went a prick of steel,
Two big brass balls filled up with cream
And the whole darn thing
Was driven by steam.

Chorus:
And the stop-cock was left handed,
And the stop-cock was left handed,
And the stop-cock was left handed,
There was no easy way to stop that thing!

This brave young girl had plenty of pluck,
She opened her legs and her body shook,
She lay on the bed demanding a fuck
And he took her hand and wished her luck.

Chorus:
And the stop-cock was left handed,
And the stop-cock was left handed,
And the stop-cock was left handed,
There was no easy way to stop that thing!

Round and round went the
Bloody great wheel,
And in and out went the prick of steel,
Down and down went the level of cream.
And up, up, up went the level of steam,

Chorus:
And the stop-cock was left handed,
And the stop-cock was left handed,
And the stop-cock was left handed,
There was no easy way to stop that thing!

She confessed, "I'm loving this,
I'm coming so much that I need to piss
And then at last the maiden cried,
"Enough! Enough! I am satisfied!"

Chorus:
And the stop-cock was left handed,
And the stop-cock was left handed,
And the stop-cock was left handed,
There was no easy way to stop that thing!

It was going like the piston of a railroad train,
He should have fitted a gearing chain,
The poor girl screamed out loud in pain,
But the dastardly dick went in again.

Chorus:
And the stop-cock was left handed,
And the stop-cock was left handed,
And the stop-cock was left handed,
There was no easy way to stop that thing!

Now we come to the tragic bit,
There was no way of stopping it,
She was split from her ass to tit,
And the whole darn thing
Was covered in shit.

Chorus:
And the stop-cock was left handed,
And the stop-cock was left handed,
And the stop-cock was left handed,
There was no easy way to stop that thing!

The moral of this story is very, very clear...
Never trust a small-cocked, fucking engineer!

MY FAVOURITE THINGS

The hills will certainly be alive with the uplifting sounds of 'Big Tits and Little Tits'. Oh, how imaginative!

Sing to the tune of:
My Favourite Things from The Sound of Music.

Big tits and little tits
And muffs with no hair on,
Pink frilly knickers,
Being caught with a hard on,
Wanking and spanking,
Being tied up with string,
These are a few of my favourite things.

Chorus:
When my balls ache,
When my ring stings,
When I'm feeling sad,
I simply remember
My favourite things,
And then I don't feel so sad.

Transvestites and perverts
All dressed in white satin,
Five dollar whores
And girls from Prestatyn,
Seedy Motel rooms
All filled with smoke rings,
These are a few of my favourite things.

Big tits and little tits,
And ones with pert nipples,
WRENS with fat faces
All covered in dimples,
Small tits that stand up,
And big one's that swing,
These are a few of my favourite things.

Chorus:
When my balls ache,
When my ring stings,
When I'm feeling sad,
I simply remember
My favourite things,
And then I don't feel so sad.

WRAFS and Welshmen
Who wear rubber wellies,
Girls in French knickers,
And slags from New Delhi,
Bras and suspenders
And tassels that swing,
These are a few of my favourite things.

Groping and stroking
Old maids in the parlour,
Licking the milkmaid
Whilst wanking the farmer,
Shagging a cockerel
Whilst clipping it's wings,
These are a few of my favourite things.

Chorus:
When my balls ache,
When my ring stings,
When I'm feeling sad,
I simply remember
My favourite things,
And then I don't feel so sad.

Hookers and scrum halves
Who love hairy asses,
Fly halves and centres
Who kiss between passes,
Wingers who can catch
And full backs that sing,
These are a few of my favourite things.

Tip socks and Gust locks
And Static Vent Covers,
Greenies and Pinkies and
Bombheads and Grubbers,
Gossamer Durex and
Hot sweaty minge,
These are a few of my favourite things.

Chorus:
When my balls ache,
When my ring stings,
When I'm feeling sad,
I simply remember
My favourite things,
And then I don't feel so sad.

Big tits and little tits
And little tits and big tits,
Little tits and big tits
And big tits and little tits,
Little tits that wobble
And big tits that swing,
These are a few of my favourite things.

Chorus:
When my balls ache,
When my ring stings,
When I'm feeling sad,
I simply remember
My favourite things,
And then I don't feel... so sad!